Amazing Weekly Workouts for Year 5!

This CGP book is bursting with speedy 10-Minute Workouts that are great for warm-ups, recaps, homework and more.

Each Workout is focused on building pupils' Arithmetic skills with more challenging questions introduced throughout the book. By the end of Year 5, there'll be no stopping them!

We've even included cut-out-and-keep answers, plus a useful progress chart to keep track of their marks.

How to Use this Book

- This book contains <u>36 workouts</u>. We've split them into <u>3 sections</u> — one for each term, with <u>12 workouts</u> each. There's roughly one workout for <u>every week</u> of the school year.

- Each workout is out of <u>16 marks</u> and should take about <u>10 minutes</u>.

- Each workout starts with some <u>Quick Fire questions</u>, which are a perfect <u>warm-up</u> before the main questions.

- The <u>first 3 workouts</u> only contain <u>Year 4 Arithmetic content</u> — they're ideal for <u>reminding</u> pupils what they learnt in the <u>previous year</u>. These workouts should be done at the <u>start</u> of Year 5.

- The <u>final 3 workouts</u> cover all of the <u>Year 5 Arithmetic content</u> — they're a great way to <u>recap</u> the year, and ensure that pupils have <u>got to grips</u> with the Year 5 topics.

- New topics are <u>gradually introduced</u>, and then <u>re-tested</u> throughout the later workouts. The workouts <u>increase in difficulty</u> as you progress.

- The <u>contents pages</u> show you where each Arithmetic topic is <u>first introduced</u>.

- The <u>tick boxes</u> on the contents pages can help you to keep a <u>record</u> of which workouts have been attempted.

- A <u>Puzzle page</u>, <u>cut-out Answers</u> and a <u>Progress Chart</u> can be found at the <u>back</u> of the book.

Published by CGP
ISBN: 978 1 78908 470 2

Editors: Adam Bartlett, Sean McParland,
      Caley Simpson, Ben Train,
      Michael Weynberg

With thanks to Michael Bushell and
Maxine Petrie for the proofreading.

With thanks to Lottie Edwards
for the copyright research.

Clipart from Corel®

Contains public sector information licensed under the Open Government Licence v3.0 http://www.nationalarchives.gov.uk/doc/open-government-licence/version/3/

Printed by Bell and Bain, Glasgow.

Based on the classic CGP style created by Richard Parsons.

Text, design, layout and original illustrations
© Coordination Group Publications Ltd. (CGP) 2020
All rights reserved.

Contents — Autumn Term

Contents — Spring Term

Contents — Summer Term

10

Quick Fire

Try to work out the answers to these in your head.

1. a) $2 \times 6 =$ ....

    b) $6 \times 6 =$ ....

    c) $9 \times 6 =$ ....

    d) $11 \times 6 =$ ....

    2 marks

2. a) .... $\div 9 = 3$

    b) .... $\div 9 = 5$

    c) .... $\div 9 = 9$

    d) .... $\div 9 = 12$

    4 marks

Now try these:

3. Count **forwards** in steps of 25 to fill in the blanks.

    75   100   200

    2 marks

4. Write these fractions as decimals:

    a) $\frac{1}{4} =$ ....

    b) $\frac{1}{2} =$ ....

    c) $\frac{3}{4} =$ ....

    2 marks

5. Work out:

a) $\dfrac{11}{8} - \dfrac{4}{8} = \dfrac{\boxed{}}{\boxed{}}$

b) $\dfrac{15}{12} - \dfrac{8}{12} = \dfrac{\boxed{}}{\boxed{}}$

2 marks

6. Put the numbers below in order from **smallest** to **largest**.

945   1310   1307   911

....

smallest   largest

2 marks

7. Work out:

a) 6472 + 2352

```
  6 4 7 2
+ 2 3 5 2
─────────

─────────
```

b) 4231 + 825

```
  4 2 3 1
+   8 2 5
─────────

─────────
```

2 marks

How did you do?

Score: ☐

(10)

Quick Fire

Try to work out the answers to these in your head.

1. a) $84 \times 1 =$ ....

    b) $108 \times 0 =$ ....

    c) $59 \div 1 =$ ....

    d) $91 \div 91 =$ ....

    _____
    2 marks

2. a) .... $\times 7 = 14$

    b) .... $\times 7 = 21$

    c) .... $\times 7 = 56$

    d) .... $\times 7 = 84$

    _____
    4 marks

Now try these:

3. Count **backwards** in steps of 6 to fill in the blanks.

    12   6   ....   −12   ....

    _____
    2 marks

4. Fill in the missing number:

    a) $8 \times 13 =$ .... $\times 8$

    b) .... $\times 4 = 4 \times 15$

    _____
    2 marks

4

5. The following sequence of numbers goes **forwards** in equal steps. Fill in the missing numbers.

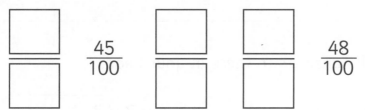

2 marks

6. Work out:

a) $18 \div 10 =$ ....

b) $7 \div 10 =$ ....

2 marks

7. Work out:

a) 61×8

```
   6 1
×    8
_____

_____
```

b) 28×7

2 marks

How did you do?

Score: [　　]

10

Quick Fire

Try to work out the answers to these in your head.

1. a) $2 \times 4 \times 3 =$ ....

    b) $4 \times 3 \times 3 =$ ....

    c) $1 \times 9 \times 5 =$ ....

    d) $4 \times 10 \times 0 =$ ....

    _____
    4 marks

2. a) .... $\div 12 = 2$

    b) .... $\div 12 = 4$

    c) .... $\div 12 = 9$

    d) .... $\div 12 = 12$

    _____
    2 marks

Now try these:

3. Count **forwards** in steps of 9 to fill in the blanks.

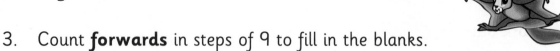

99   108   126   144

_____
1 mark

4. Fill in the boxes with **>** or **<** to make the sentences true.

    a) 4572 ☐ 4589

    b) 7364 ☐ 7368

    _____
    2 marks

6

5. What is 9246 – 5437?

$$
\begin{array}{r}
9\ 2\ 4\ 6 \\
-\ 5\ 4\ 3\ 7 \\
\hline
 \\
\hline
\end{array}
$$

1 mark

6. Fill in the boxes with **>** or **<** to make the sentences true.

   a) 1.26 ☐ 2.01

   b) 1.18 ☐ 1.14

2 marks

7. Work out:

   a) 9 – 1.8 = ...

   b) 6 – 3.8 = ...

2 marks

8. Work out:

   a) 282 × 3

   b) 191 × 7

$$
\begin{array}{r}
2\ 8\ 2 \\
\times\ \ \ \ \ 3 \\
\hline
 \\
\hline
\end{array}
$$

2 marks

How did you do?

Score: ☐

Quick Fire

Try to work out the answers to these in your head.

1. a) 3 × 8 = ...

    b) 7 × 11 = ...

    c) 6 × 10 = ...

    d) 12 × 4 = ...

    2 marks

2. a) 15 ÷ 10 = ...

    b) 64 ÷ 10 = ...

    c) 30 ÷ 10 = ...

    d) 8 ÷ 10 = ...

    4 marks

Now try these:

3. Count **backwards** in steps of 1000 to fill in the blanks.

    27 105   26 105   ....

    2 marks

4. Use partitioning to fill in the missing numbers.
    An example is shown below.

    14 × 8 = ..10.. × 8 + ..4.. × 8 = ..80.. + ..32.. = 112

    a) 15 × 3 = ... × 3 + ... × 3 = ... + ... = ...

    b) 21 × 4 = ... × 4 + ... × 4 = ... + ... = ...

    2 marks

5. Put the numbers below in order from **smallest** to **largest**.

7.3   8.2   7.7   8.0   7.8

....
smallest   largest

_____
2 marks

6. Write these fractions as decimals:

a) $\frac{1}{10}$ = ...

b) $\frac{4}{10}$ = ...

c) $\frac{7}{10}$ = ...

d) $\frac{9}{10}$ = ...

_____
2 marks

7. Work out:

a) 4658 – 2164   b) 9136 – 4595

```
   4 6 5 8
 - 2 1 6 4
 _____


 _____
```

_____
2 marks

How did you do?   **Score:** [ ]

Quick Fire

Try to work out the answers to these in your head.

1. a) $36 \div 4 =$ ....

    c) $84 \div 12 =$ ....

    b) $64 \div 8 =$ ....

    d) $108 \div 9 =$ ....

    _____
    2 marks

2. a) $3 \times 5 \times 2 =$ ....

    c) $12 \times 0 \times 7 =$ ....

    b) $11 \times 1 \times 8 =$ ....

    d) $7 \times 3 \times 3 =$ ....

    _____
    4 marks

Now try these:

3. Work out:

    a) $50\ 227 + 14\ 261$

    ```
      5 0 2 2 7
    + 1 4 2 6 1
    _____
    ```

    b) $64\ 280 + 27\ 231$

    ```
      6 4 2 8 0
    + 2 7 2 3 1
    _____
    ```

    _____
    2 marks

4. Count **backwards** in steps of 7 to fill in the blanks.

    14   7   0   ....   –21

    _____
    1 mark

5. Round the numbers below to the nearest 1000:

   a) 12 386 ....

   b) 568 531 ....

   c) 749 662 ....

6. Fill in the boxes with **>** or **<** to make the sentences true.

   a) 18.61 ☐ 18.37   b) 10.66 ☐ 10.57

7. Work out:

   a) 128 × 5   b) 871 × 7

```
    1 2 8
  ×     5
  _____

  _____
```

How did you do?

Score: ☐

10

Quick Fire

Try to work out the answers to these in your head.

1. a) $6 \times 4 =$ ....
    b) $7 \times 7 =$ ....

    c) $9 \times 6 =$ ....
    d) $12 \times 3 =$ ....

    2 marks

2. a) $145 \times 1 =$ ....
    b) $384 \times 0 =$ ....

    c) $488 \div 1 =$ ....
    d) $237 \div 237 =$ ....

    2 marks

Now try these:

3. Work out:

    a) $7000 + 2000 =$ ....

    b) $1600 + 5100 =$ ....

    c) $3450 + 4500 =$ ....

    3 marks

4. Round the numbers below to the nearest 100:

    a) 48 526   ....
    b) 397 055   ....

    2 marks

12

5. Give your answers to the calculations below as mixed numbers.

a) $\dfrac{12}{7} + \dfrac{15}{7} =$ ☐ ☐/☐

b) $\dfrac{14}{5} + \dfrac{8}{5} =$ ☐ ☐/☐

2 marks

6. Count **backwards** in steps of 1000 to fill in the blanks.

152 844   151 844   ....

2 marks

7. Work out:

a) 5400 – 3000 = ...

b) 7100 – 2300 = ...

c) 5070 – 4500 = ...

3 marks

How did you do?

Score: ☐

Quick Fire

Try to work out the answers to these in your head.

1. a) $4 \times 9 =$ ....

    b) $5 \times 8 =$ ....

    c) $11 \times 5 =$ ....

    d) $9 \times 12 =$ ....

    _____
    2 marks

2. a) $6 \div 10 =$ ....

    b) $93 \div 10 =$ ....

    c) $71 \div 100 =$ ....

    d) $2 \div 100 =$ ....

    _____
    4 marks

Now try these:

3. Work out:

    a) $63\,837 - 13\,044$

    b) $53\,982 - 33\,796$

```
      6 3 8 3 7              5 3 9 8 2
    – 1 3 0 4 4            – 3 3 7 9 6
    _____            _____

    _____            _____
```
    _____
    2 marks

4. Round the numbers below to the nearest 1000:

    a) 72 187 ....

    b) 846 702 ....

    _____
    2 marks

14

5. The following sequence of numbers goes **backwards** in steps of 1000. Fill in the missing numbers.

.... 340 551 .... 337 551

2 marks

6. Round the decimals below to the nearest whole number:

a) 1.3 ....

b) 23.8 ....

2 marks

7. Work out:

a) 903 × 3

b) 451 × 9

```
    9 0 3
  ×     3
  _____

  _____
```

2 marks

How did you do?

Score:

10

Quick Fire

Try to work out the answers to these in your head.

1. a) $12 \div 3 =$ ....
   b) $21 \div 3 =$ ....

   c) $27 \div 3 =$ ....
   d) $36 \div 3 =$ ....

   _____
   2 marks

2. a) $2 \times 6 \times 4 =$ ....
   b) $11 \times 1 \times 2 =$ ....

   c) $9 \times 3 \times 2 =$ ....
   d) $10 \times 75 \times 0 =$ ....

   _____
   4 marks

Now try these:

3. Count **forwards** in steps of 100 000 to fill in the blanks.

   129 024   229 024   ....

   _____
   2 marks

4. Put the numbers below in order from **largest** to **smallest**.

   32 507   31 597   41 386   32 497   31 589

   ....
   largest   smallest

   _____
   2 marks

5. Give your answers to the calculations below as mixed numbers.

a) $\dfrac{24}{9} - \dfrac{11}{9} =$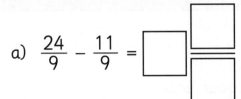

b) $\dfrac{41}{6} - \dfrac{34}{6} =$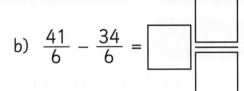

6. Write these fractions as decimals:

a) $\dfrac{1}{100} =$ ....

b) $\dfrac{7}{100} =$ ....

c) $\dfrac{45}{100} =$ ....

7. Work out:

a) 42 148 + 26 508

b) 94 254 + 37 316

```
    4 2 1 4 8
 +  2 6 5 0 8
 _____


 _____
```

How did you do?

Score:

Quick Fire

Try to work out the answers to these in your head.

1. a) 2300 + 2000 = ...   b) 4800 + 3000 = ...

    c) 6340 + 3100 = ...   d) 1687 + 5300 = ...

                                                                    2 marks

2. a) 8400 – 6000 = ...   b) 5620 – 3000 = ...

    c) 7704 – 5600 = ...   d) 4782 – 4400 = ...

                                                                    2 marks

Now try these:

3. Work out:

    a) 590 330 + 243 424   b) 382 160 + 319 156

    ```
      5 9 0 3 3 0                        3 8 2 1 6 0
    + 2 4 3 4 2 4                      + 3 1 9 1 5 6
    _____                       _____
    ```

                                                                    2 marks

4. What is 545 627 rounded to the nearest:

    a) 10? ....   b) 1000? ....

                                                                    2 marks

5. Fill in the boxes with **>** or **<** to make the sentences true.

a) 32.7 ☐ 34.7

b) 81.34 ☐ 81.36

2 marks

6. Work out:

a) 4.2 + 3.9 = ...

b) 7.2 – 2.6 = ...

2 marks

7. Put the numbers below in order from **smallest** to **largest**.

94 212   88 302   94 221   89 201   88 401

....

smallest   largest

2 marks

8. Work out:

a) 292 × 3   b) 514 × 6

```
  2 9 2
×     3
_____

_____
```

2 marks

How did you do?   **Score:** ☐

Quick Fire

Try to work out the answers to these in your head.

1. a) $250 \div 5 =$ ....

    b) $400 \div 5 =$ ....

    c) $525 \div 5 =$ ....

    d) $605 \div 5 =$ ....

    2 marks

2. a) $15 \div$ .... $= 1.5$

    b) $6 \div$ .... $= 0.06$

    c) $9 \div$ .... $= 0.9$

    d) $78 \div$ .... $= 0.78$

    4 marks

Now try these:

3. Put the numbers below in order from **smallest** to **largest**.

    814 643   814 463   816 643   814 655

    ....

    smallest   largest

    2 marks

4. Work out:

    a) $13\,000 + 12\,000 =$ ....

    b) $24\,510 + 35\,000 =$ ....

    2 marks

20

5. Count **backwards** in steps of 100 000 to fill in the blanks.

844 912 .... 644 912 ....

2 marks

6. Work out:

a) 72 700 – 32 000 = ...

b) 56 420 – 44 100 = ...

2 marks

7. Work out:

a) 36 572 – 24 534   b) 76 621 – 38 716

```
    3 6 5 7 2
  – 2 4 5 3 4
  _____

  _____
```

2 marks

How did you do?

Score:

21

10

Quick Fire

Try to work out the answers to these in your head.

1. a) $7 \times 5 =$ .... b) $6 \times 6 =$ ....

    c) $4 \times 11 =$ .... d) $8 \times 12 =$ ....

    2 marks

2. a) $3260 -$ .... $= 1260$ b) $4888 -$ .... $= 3888$

    c) $8117 -$ .... $= 2117$ d) $9839 -$ .... $= 839$

    4 marks

Now try these:

3. Work out:

    a) $378\,723 - 164\,812$ b) $445\,178 - 319\,330$

```
   3 7 8 7 2 3          4 4 5 1 7 8
 - 1 6 4 8 1 2        - 3 1 9 3 3 0
 _____          _____

 _____          _____
```

2 marks

4. The following sequence of numbers goes **forwards** in steps of 100 000. Fill in the missing numbers.

    .... 617 884   717 884   ....

    2 marks

22

5. Work out:

   a) 11 250 + 21 000 = ...

   b) 54 168 + 33 400 = ...

1 mark

6. Round the decimals below to the nearest whole number:

   a) 1.7   ....

   b) 12.5   ....

   c) 37.2   ....

3 marks

7. Work out:

   a) 712 × 5   b) 865 × 9

2 marks

How did you do?

Score:

Quick Fire

Try to work out the answers to these in your head.

1. a) $72 \div$ .... $= 0.72$ b) $5 \div$ .... $= 0.5$

    c) $22 \div$ .... $= 2.2$ d) $9 \div$ .... $= 0.09$

    _____
    4 marks

2. a) $9 \times 3 =$ ....   b) $12 \times 5 =$ ....

    c) $9 \times 7 =$ ....   d) $11 \times 12 =$ ....

    _____
    2 marks

Now try these:

3. Count **forwards** in steps of 10 000 to fill in the blanks.

    273 612   283 612   ....

    _____
    2 marks

4. Write these decimals as fractions:

    a) $0.3 = \dfrac{\boxed{}}{10}$ b) $0.9 = \dfrac{\boxed{}}{10}$

    _____
    2 marks

5. What is 849 616 rounded to the nearest:

    a) 100?   ....

    b) 1000?   ....

2 marks

6. Fill in the missing number:

    a) 154 381 − .... = 94 381

    b) .... − 70 000 = 28 822

2 marks

7. Work out:

    a) 796 632 + 138 565

    b) 809 053 + 269 847

```
   7 9 6 6 3 2
 + 1 3 8 5 6 5
 _____
```

2 marks

How did you do?

Score:

(10)

Quick Fire

Try to work out the answers to these in your head.

1. a) $5 \times 6 =$ ....
    b) $3 \times 7 =$ ....

    c) $7 \times 8 =$ ....
    d) $1 \times 4 =$ ....

    e) $9 \times 4 =$ ....
    f) $8 \times 11 =$ ....

    _____
    3 marks

2. a) $5400 - 600 =$ ....
    b) $860 - 700 =$ ....

    c) $1800 - 900 =$ ....
    d) $4000 - 400 =$ ....

    _____
    2 marks

Now try these:

3. Work out:

    a) $105 \times 10 =$ ....
    b) $4.5 \times 10 =$ ....

    c) $784 \div 10 =$ ....
    d) $20.4 \div 10 =$ ....

    _____
    4 marks

4. Work out:

    a) $10.5 + 1.306 =$ ....
    b) $4 - 1.814 =$ ....

    _____
    2 marks

5. Put the numbers below in order from smallest to largest.

    324 858   324 265   343 588   342 885

    ....
    smallest   largest

6. The following sequence of numbers goes **backwards**
    in steps of equal size. Fill in the missing numbers.

    $\dfrac{}{100}$ $\dfrac{79}{100}$ $\dfrac{}{100}$ $\dfrac{}{100}$ $\dfrac{76}{100}$

7. Work out:

    a) 916 683 – 150 342   b) 572 559 – 528 746

    ```
      9 1 6 6 8 3
    – 1 5 0 3 4 2
    ─────────────
    ```

    ```
      5 7 2 5 5 9
    – 5 2 8 7 4 6
    ─────────────
    ```

How did you do?

Score:

Quick Fire

Try to work out the answers to these in your head.

1. a) 3 240 000 + 20 000 = ...

    b) 6 510 000 – 30 000 = ...

    1 mark

2. a) 18 ÷ 9 = ... b) 32 ÷ 4 = ...

    c) 48 ÷ 6 = ... d) 72 ÷ 8 = ...

    2 marks

Now try these:

3. Work out:

    a) 438 007 + 3372

```
    4 3 8 0 0 7
  +     3 3 7 2
  _____
```

    b) 702 020 + 35 996

```
    7 0 2 0 2 0
  +   3 5 9 9 6
  _____
```

    2 marks

4. What is:

    a) 859 646 rounded to the nearest 10 000?   ....

    b) 156 368 rounded to the nearest 10 000?   ....

    c) 310 571 rounded to the nearest 10 000?   ....

    3 marks

5. The following sequence of numbers goes **forwards** in steps of 1000. Fill in the missing numbers.

.... 616 884 617 884 ....

6. Write the following decimals as fractions.

a) $0.5 = \dfrac{\boxed{}}{\boxed{}}$

b) $0.75 = \dfrac{\boxed{}}{\boxed{}}$

7. Fill in the boxes with **>** or **<** to make the sentences true.

a) 0.25 $\boxed{}$ 0.52

b) 1.7 $\boxed{}$ 1.07

8. Fill in the missing numbers.

a) $1619 -$ .... $= 919$

b) .... $- 3000 = 2465$

c) $46\ 217 -$ .... $= 41\ 217$

How did you do?

Score: $\boxed{}$

Quick Fire

Try to work out the answers to these in your head.

1. a) 10 000 + 1000 = ...

   b) 30 000 + 100 = ...

   c) 770 000 + 10 000 = ...

   d) 902 000 + 10 000 = ...

   2 marks

2. a) 77 × 0 = ...   b) 841 × 1 = ...

   c) 324 ÷ 324 = ...   d) 469 ÷ 1 = ...

   2 marks

Now try these:

3. Work out:

   a) 4.65 × 100 = ...

   b) 5600 ÷ 100 = ...

   2 marks

4. Write the following decimals as fractions.

   a) $0.67 = \dfrac{\boxed{}}{100}$ b) $0.03 = \dfrac{\boxed{}}{100}$

   2 marks

5. Work out:

a) 21.45 + 6.645

$$
\begin{array}{r}
2\ 1.4\ 5\ 0 \\
+\quad 6.6\ 4\ 5 \\
\hline
 \\
\end{array}
$$

b) 14.951 − 8.713

$$
\begin{array}{r}
1\ 4.9\ 5\ 1 \\
-\quad 8.7\ 1\ 3 \\
\hline
 \\
\end{array}
$$

2 marks

6. The following sequence of numbers goes **forwards** in steps of 10 000. Fill in the missing numbers.

....   198 509   ....   218 509

2 marks

7. Put the numbers below in order from largest to smallest.

| 0.03 | 0.3 | 0.29 | 1.3 |

....

largest   smallest

2 marks

8. Work out:

a) 401 × 4

$$
\begin{array}{r}
4\ 0\ 1 \\
\times\quad\ \ 4 \\
\hline
 \\
\end{array}
$$

b) 121 × 6

2 marks

How did you do?

Score:

Quick Fire

Try to work out the answers to these in your head.

1. a) $11 \times 7 =$ ....
    b) $7 \times 8 =$ ....

    c) $6 \times 2 =$ ....
    d) $9 \times 5 =$ ....

    _____
    2 marks

2. a) $\dfrac{3}{7} + \dfrac{6}{7} = \boxed{}\,\dfrac{\boxed{}}{\boxed{}}$
    b) $\dfrac{19}{11} + \dfrac{17}{11} = \boxed{}\,\dfrac{\boxed{}}{\boxed{}}$

    _____
    2 marks

Now try these:

3. Round the following numbers to the nearest 100 000.

    a) 246 315 → ....

    b) 691 372 → ....

    c) 156 983 → ....

    d) 760 481 → ....

    _____
    4 marks

4. Work out:

a) 72 990 – 40 143

$$\begin{array}{r} 7\,2\,9\,9\,0 \\ -\ 4\,0\,1\,4\,3 \\ \hline \end{array}$$

b) 715 493 – 2996

$$\begin{array}{r} 7\,1\,5\,4\,9\,3 \\ -\ \ \ \ \ 2\,9\,9\,6 \\ \hline \end{array}$$

2 marks

5. Work out:

a) 453.43 + 28.673

$$\begin{array}{r} 4\,5\,3.4\,3\,0 \\ +\ \ \ 2\,8.6\,7\,3 \\ \hline \end{array}$$

b) 638.754 + 178.21

2 marks

6. Work out:

a) 850 × 3

$$\begin{array}{r} 8\,5\,0 \\ \times\ \ \ \ \ 3 \\ \hline \end{array}$$

b) 132 × 7

2 marks

7. The following sequence of numbers goes **forwards** in steps of 9. Fill in the missing numbers.

....   –15   12

2 marks

How did you do?   Score: [   ]

33

Quick Fire

Try to work out the answers to these in your head.

1. a) $6 \times 4 =$ ....   b) $9 \times 9 =$ ....

    c) $3 \times 8 =$ ....   d) $7 \times 11 =$ ....

    2 marks

2. a) $600 \div 5 =$ ....   b) $72\,000 \div 80 =$ ....

    1 mark

Now try these:

3. Work out:

    a) $3.67 \times 1000 =$ ....   b) $0.68 \times 1000 =$ ....

    c) $4580 \div 1000 =$ ....   d) $360 \div 1000 =$ ....

    4 marks

4. Work out:

    a) 8467×2

    ```
        8 4 6 7
    ×         2
    ─────────────
    ```

    b) 9315×4

    ```
        9 3 1 5
    ×         4
    ─────────────
    ```

    2 marks

5. Put the numbers below in order from largest to smallest.

267 109   276 109   267 190   297 106

....

largest   smallest

6. Write the following decimals as fractions.

a) 0.43 =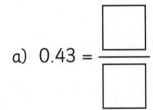

b) 0.67 =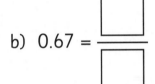

7. What is 985.791 – 606.493?

```
  9 8 5.7 9 1
– 6 0 6.4 9 3
```

8. Work out:

a) 311 982 + 30 566

```
  3 1 1 9 8 2
+   3 0 5 6 6
```

b) 241 232 + 4870

```
  2 4 1 2 3 2
+     4 8 7 0
```

How did you do?   Score:

10

Quick Fire

Try to work out the answers to these in your head.

1. a) 53 000 + 14 000 = ...

    b) 32 000 + 62 000 = ...

    2 marks

2. a) 54 ÷ 10 = ...   b) 90 ÷ 100 = ...

    c) 21 ÷ 100 = ...   d) 6 ÷ 10 = ...

    4 marks

Now try these:

3. Work out:

    a) 936 ÷ 3   b) 786 ÷ 6

    3 | 9 3 6   6 | 7 8 6

    2 marks

4. Count **backwards** in steps of 10 000 to fill in the gaps.

    428 556   418 556   ....

    1 mark

36

5. Work out:

a) 359 326 – 76 309

$$
\begin{array}{r}
3\ 5\ 9\ 3\ 2\ 6 \\
-\quad 7\ 6\ 3\ 0\ 9 \\
\hline
\end{array}
$$

b) 934 143 – 9690

6. Round the following numbers to the nearest 10 000.

a) 659 475 → ....

b) 943 563 → ....

c) 553 156 → ....

7. Put the numbers below in order from smallest to largest.

79 488   79 498   79 398   79 484

....
smallest   largest

How did you do?   **Score:**

Spring Term: Workout 7

Quick Fire

Try to work out the answers to these in your head.

1. a) 146 000 – 4000 = ...

   b) 55 300 – 22 000 = ...

2 marks

2. Count **forwards** in steps of 4 to fill in the missing numbers.

   –12   –8   ....

1 mark

Now try these:

3. Put the fractions below in order from smallest to largest.

   $\frac{7}{10}$ $\frac{8}{15}$ $\frac{4}{5}$

   $\frac{\square}{\square}$ $\frac{\square}{\square}$ $\frac{\square}{\square}$

   smallest   largest

2 marks

4. Work out:

   a) $20 \times 9 =$ ....

   b) $6 \times 400 =$ ....

   c) $70 \times 80 =$ ....

   d) $40 \times 700 =$ ....

4 marks

5. Round the following numbers to the nearest 100 000.

   a) $445\ 564 \rightarrow$ ....

   b) $695\ 457 \rightarrow$ ....

2 marks

6. What fraction of the shape below is shaded?
   Give your answer in its simplest form.

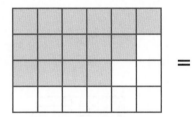 

1 mark

7. Work out:

   a) .... $\times\ 10 = 4800$

   b) .... $\times\ 10 = 15$

   c) .... $\div\ 10 = 304$

   d) .... $\div\ 10 = 0.89$

4 marks

How did you do?

Score:

Quick Fire

Try to work out the answers to these in your head.

1. a) 4 × 3 = ...   b) 5 × 8 = ...

    c) 7 × 12 = ...   d) 11 × 2 = ...

    e) 3 × 7 = ...   f) 8 × 4 = ...

                                                                    _____
                                                                    3 marks

2. a) 6235 + 1000 = ...   b) 2515 + 3000 = ...

    c) 2460 + 7300 = ...   d) 2124 + 5800 = ...
                                                                    _____
                                                                    2 marks

Now try these:

3. Tick the two shapes which have $\frac{3}{10}$ shaded.

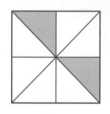      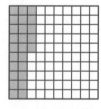

☐   ☐   ☐

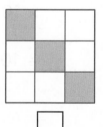   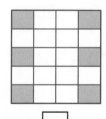

☐   ☐

                                                                    _____
                                                                    2 marks

4. Work out:

a) 74 524 + 987

b) 547 637 + 8970

$$\begin{array}{r} 7\ 4\ 5\ 2\ 4 \\ +\ \ \ \ \ 9\ 8\ 7 \\ \hline \end{array}$$

2 marks

5. The following sequence of numbers goes **backwards** in steps of 100 000. Fill in the missing numbers.

.... 503 848 .... 303 848 _____

2 marks

6. Work out:

a) 150.04 + 30.02 = ...

b) 0.51 + 55.46 = ...

c) 800.6 + 6.007 = ...

3 marks

7. Work out:

a) 236 ÷ 4

b) 875 ÷ 7

$$4\ \overline{)2\ 3\ 6}$$

$$7\ \overline{)8\ 7\ 5}$$

2 marks

How did you do?

Score:

(10)

Quick Fire

Try to work out the answers to these in your head.

1. a) 606 000 + 4000 = ...

    b) 984 000 + 9000 = ...

    c) 788 000 + 10 700 = ...

    _____
    3 marks

2. a) 27 ÷ 9 = ...   b) 24 ÷ 4 = ...

    c) 63 ÷ 7 = ...   d) 48 ÷ 12 = ...

    _____
    2 marks

Now try these:

3. The diagrams below show three equivalent fractions.

     = =

    Fill in the missing values.

    $\frac{2}{5}$ = $\dfrac{\boxed{}}{10}$ = $\dfrac{\boxed{}}{50}$

    _____
    2 marks

4. Work out:

   a) 542 ÷ 3

   b) 177 ÷ 9

   $$3 \overline{)\, 5\ 4\ 2}\ ^r$$

   $$9 \overline{)\, 1\ 7\ 7}\ ^r$$

   _____
   2 marks

5. Fill in the missing numbers.

   a) .... × 100 = 260

   b) .... ÷ 100 = 10.6

   _____
   2 marks

6. Write the following decimals as fractions.

   a) $0.7 = \dfrac{\boxed{}}{\boxed{}}$

   b) $0.47 = \dfrac{\boxed{}}{\boxed{}}$

   c) $0.09 = \dfrac{\boxed{}}{\boxed{}}$

   _____
   3 marks

7. Work out:

   a) 7459 × 3

   $$\begin{array}{r} 7\ 4\ 5\ 9 \\ \times \quad\ \ 3 \\ \hline \\ \hline \end{array}$$

   b) 4674 × 8

   $$\begin{array}{r} 4\ 6\ 7\ 4 \\ \times \quad\ \ 8 \\ \hline \\ \hline \end{array}$$

   _____
   2 marks

How did you do?

Score: [ ]

Spring Term: Workout 9

Quick Fire

Try to work out the answers to these in your head.

1. a) 1736 + 500 = ...   b) 2408 + 600 = ...

    c) 5572 + 800 = ...   d) 8907 + 900 = ...

_____
2 marks

2. a) 15.7 × 10 = ...   b) 38.1 ÷ 10 = ...

_____
2 marks

Now try these:

3. Work out:

    a) 5 − 10 = ...   b) −6 + 4 = ...

    c) −4 − 3 = ...   d) 7 − 9 = ...

_____
4 marks

4. Work out:

    a) 1128 ÷ 2   b) 8952 ÷ 6

     2 | 1 1 2 8   6 | 8 9 5 2

_____
2 marks

5. Put the fractions below in order from largest to smallest.

$$\frac{3}{4} \qquad \frac{1}{2} \qquad \frac{11}{16} \qquad \frac{5}{8}$$

largest   smallest

2 marks

6. Work out:

a) $62\ 716 - 3345$

$$
\begin{array}{r}
6\ 2\ 7\ 1\ 6 \\
-\ \ \ 3\ 3\ 4\ 5 \\
\hline
\end{array}
$$

b) $330\ 357 - 9259$

2 marks

7. Fill in the missing values in these equivalent fractions.

a) $\dfrac{3}{8} = \dfrac{\boxed{}}{24}$

b) $\dfrac{4}{5} = \dfrac{\boxed{}}{25}$

2 marks

How did you do?

Score:

(10)

Quick Fire

Try to work out the answers to these in your head.

1. a) $4.09 \times 10 =$ ....

    b) $0.23 \times 100 =$ ....

    c) $81.6 \times 10 =$ ....

    d) $9.86 \times 100 =$ ....

    _____
    2 marks

2. a) $465\ 623 + 30\ 000 =$ ....

    b) $187\ 414 + 600\ 000 =$ ....

    _____
    1 mark

Now try these:

3. Convert the following mixed numbers into improper fractions.

    a) $1\frac{1}{2} = \dfrac{\boxed{}}{2}$

    b) $2\frac{3}{4} = \dfrac{\boxed{}}{4}$

    c) $5\frac{2}{3} = \dfrac{\boxed{}}{3}$

    _____
    3 marks

4. Work out:

    a) 312×25

    ```
        3 1 2
    ×     2 5
    _____

    +
    _____
    _____
    ```

    b) 163×46

    ```
        1 6 3
    ×     4 6
    _____

    +
    _____
    _____
    ```

    _____
    2 marks

5. Shade in $\frac{7}{10}$ of each shape below.

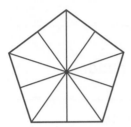

2 marks

6. Work out:

a) 2800 ÷ 7 = ...

b) 270 ÷ 9 = ...

c) 3600 ÷ 400 = ...

d) 5400 ÷ 90 = ...

4 marks

7. Work out:

a) 8 – 20 = ...

b) –6 – 11 = ...

2 marks

How did you do?

Score:

Spring Term: Workout 12

Quick Fire

Try to work out the answers to these in your head.

1. a) $19 \times 2 =$ ....   b) $14 \times 5 =$ ....

    c) $4 \times 16 =$ ....   d) $3 \times 13 =$ ....

    2 marks

2. Round the numbers below to the nearest whole number.

    a) $6.4 =$ ....   b) $4.5 =$ ....

    2 marks

Now try these:

3. Work out:

    a) $\dfrac{1}{2} + \dfrac{1}{8} = \dfrac{\boxed{}}{\boxed{}}$ b) $\dfrac{11}{15} - \dfrac{3}{5} = \dfrac{\boxed{}}{\boxed{}}$

    2 marks

4. Work out:

    a) $2348 \div 3$ b) $7165 \div 7$

    $$3\overline{\smash{\big)}2\ 3\ 4\ 8}^{\;r}$$ $$7\overline{\smash{\big)}7\ 1\ 6\ 5}^{\;r}$$

    2 marks

5. Fill in the missing numbers.

a) .... × 1000 = 9800

b) .... ÷ 1000 = 81

c) .... × 1000 = 90

6. Work out:

a) 808 771 + 517 498

$$
\begin{array}{r}
8\,0\,8\,7\,7\,1 \\
+\,5\,1\,7\,4\,9\,8 \\
\hline
\end{array}
$$

b) 783 545 + 131 984

7. Fill in the missing value in this equivalent fraction.

$$\frac{4}{7} = \frac{\boxed{}}{28}$$

8. Convert the following mixed numbers into improper fractions.

a) $2\frac{5}{7} = \dfrac{\boxed{}}{\boxed{}}$

b) $4\frac{2}{5} = \dfrac{\boxed{}}{\boxed{}}$

How did you do?

Score: [ ]

Quick Fire

Try to work out the answers to these in your head.

1. a) 5 × 6 = ...

    b) 3 × 9 = ...

    c) 4 × 12 = ...

    d) 6 × 7 = ...

    e) 8 × 8 = ...

    f) 12 × 11 = ...

    _____
    3 marks

2. a) 4217 + 1000 = ...

    b) 7434 + 2000 = ...

    c) 2001 + 7000 = ...

    d) 5703 + 3000 = ...

    _____
    2 marks

Now try these:

3. What is $3 \times \frac{3}{5}$? Use the picture below to help you.

$3 \times \frac{3}{5} =$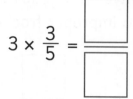

_____
1 mark

4. The following sequence of numbers goes **backwards** in steps of 100 000. Fill in the missing numbers.

    .... 449 711 .... 149 711

    _____
    2 marks

5. Round these numbers to the nearest 10 000.

   a) 342 743 → ....

   b) 195 262 → ....

   c) 849 033 → ....

   d) 746 352 → ....

4 marks

6. Work out:

   a) 172.106 + 65.895   b) 831.178 – 42.54

2 marks

7. Work out:

   a) 83 870 – 4321   b) 961 715 + 27 256

2 marks

How did you do?   **Score:**

10

Try to work out the answers to these in your head.

1. a) $24 \div 6 =$ ....

    b) $48 \div 4 =$ ....

    c) $84 \div 12 =$ ....

    d) $81 \div 9 =$ ....

    e) $40 \div 8 =$ ....

    f) $132 \div 11 =$ ....

    _____
    3 marks

2. a) $-2 + 6 =$ ....

    b) $2 - 7 =$ ....

    c) $9 - 12 =$ ....

    d) $-7 + 15 =$ ....

    _____
    2 marks

Now try these:

3. Round these decimals to the nearest whole number:

    a) 0.51 rounds to ....

    b) 3.35 rounds to ....

    _____
    2 marks

4. Fill in the missing numbers in the calculation below.

    $$\frac{8}{9} + \frac{5}{9} = \frac{\boxed{}}{9} = \boxed{}\frac{\boxed{}}{9}$$

    _____
    1 mark

5. Work out:

    a) 153 × 18

        $$\begin{array}{r} 1\ 5\ 3 \\ \times\quad 1\ 8 \\ \hline \\ \end{array}$$

        +
        _____

        _____

    b) 342 × 24

6. Put the fractions below in order from smallest to largest.

    $\frac{1}{4}$ $\frac{3}{8}$ $\frac{5}{16}$ $\frac{1}{2}$

       [ ]

    smallest   largest

7. The following sequence of numbers goes **forwards**
    in steps of 10 000. Fill in the missing numbers.

    ....   18 549   ....   48 549

8. Work out:

    a) 417 ÷ 3   b) 952 ÷ 4

How did you do?    Score: [   ]

Quick Fire

Try to work out the answers to these in your head.

1. a) $9 \times 7 =$ ....   b) $55 \div 11 =$ ....

    c) $60 \div 12 =$ ....   d) $12 \times 12 =$ ....

_____
2 marks

2. a) 660 115 − 40 000 = ...

    b) 909 338 − 600 000 = ...

_____
2 marks

Now try these:

3. Work out:

    a) $5^2 = 5 \times 5 =$ ....

    b) $8^2 = 8 \times 8 =$ ....

_____
2 marks

4. What is $4 \times 1\frac{2}{3}$? Write your answer as
    a mixed number in its simplest form.

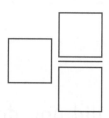

_____
1 mark

5. Count **backwards** in steps of 1000 to fill in the blanks.

33 209 .... 29 209

6. Round these numbers to the nearest 100 000.

    a) 949 999 rounds to ....

    b) 531 102 rounds to ....

    c) 658 235 rounds to ....

7. Work out:

    a) 2764 ÷ 4   b) 3321 ÷ 9

    4 | 2 7 6 4   9 | 3 3 2 1

8. Count **forwards** in steps of 10 000 to fill in the blanks.

389 .... 40 389

How did you do?   Score: [   ]

Quick Fire

Try to work out the answers to these in your head.

1. a) $6 \times 8 =$ ....
    b) $64 \div 8 =$ ....
    c) $96 \div 8 =$ ....
    d) $11 \times 8 =$ ....

    _____
    2 marks

2. a) $4 \times 12 \div 1 =$ ....
    b) $42 \times 6 \times 0 =$ ....
    c) $0 \times 56 \times 1 =$ ....
    d) $7 \times 9 \times 1 =$ ....

    _____
    2 marks

Now try these:

3. Round these numbers to 1 decimal place.

    a) 3.29 rounds to ....

    b) 7.14 rounds to ....

    c) 6.25 rounds to ....

    _____
    3 marks

4. Work out:

    a) $2^3 = 2 \times 2 \times 2 =$ ....

    b) $4^3 = 4 \times 4 \times 4 =$ ....

    _____
    2 marks

5. Fill in the missing equivalent fractions
    and shade in the diagrams to match.

    $$\frac{2}{3} = \frac{\boxed{}}{9} = \frac{12}{\boxed{}}$$

6. Put the numbers below in order from **smallest** to **largest**.

    5   −7   1   −2   3

    ....
    smallest   largest

7. Work out:

    a) 9 × 1000 = ...

    b) 0.9 × 100 = ...

    c) 900 ÷ 1000 = ...

How did you do?   Score: [   ]

Summer Term: Workout 5

Quick Fire

Try to work out the answers to these in your head.

1. a) $2 \times 3 \times 4 =$ ....

   b) $5 \times 2 \times 8 =$ ....

   c) $11 \times 12 \times 1 =$ ....

   d) $9 \times 0 \times 10 =$ ....

   _____
   2 marks

2. a) $7300 - 2000 =$ ....

   b) $3880 - 700 =$ ....

   c) $6808 - 500 =$ ....

   d) $9919 - 8 =$ ....

   _____
   2 marks

3. a) $112\ 530 + 57\ 000 =$ ....

   b) $632\ 505 + 240\ 000 =$ ....

   _____
   2 marks

Now try these:

4. Work out:

   a) 1385×33

   b) 2053×24

```
      1 3 8 5
   ×     3 3
   _____


   + _____
   _____
```

_____
2 marks

5. How many thousandths are there in:

   a) 1 hundredth? ....

   b) 1 tenth? ....

   c) 10 hundredths? ....

3 marks

6. Fill in the missing numbers in the calculation below.

$$\frac{6}{7} + \frac{6}{7} = \boxed{}\,\frac{\boxed{}}{7}$$

1 mark

7. Write the decimal equivalents of these numbers.

   a) 12 thousandths = ...

   b) 270 thousandths = ...

2 marks

8. Work out:
   a) 47 353 − 12 161   b) 725 586 − 34 351

2 marks

How did you do?   Score: [ ]

Quick Fire

Try to work out the answers to these in your head.

1. a) $24 \div 10 = $ ....
    b) $36 \div 100 = $ ....

    c) $198 \div 100 = $ ....
    d) $5 \div 1000 = $ ....

    2 marks

2. a) $9 - 18 = $ ....
    b) $-15 + 23 = $ ....

    c) $-7 + 7 = $ ....
    d) $14 - 21 = $ ....

    2 marks

Now try these:

3. Fill in the boxes with **>** or **<** to make each sentence true.

    46.779 ☐ 46.778

    3.14 ☐ 3.141

    2 marks

4. Work out:

    a) $3^2 = $ ....
    b) $7^2 = $ ....

    2 marks

5. Put the numbers below in order from **largest** to **smallest**.

21.429   21.43   21.349   21.493

....

largest   smallest

2 marks

6. Convert these mixed numbers into improper fractions.

a) $1\frac{6}{11} = $ ⬜⬜   b) $2\frac{5}{7} = $ ⬜⬜   c) $4\frac{3}{4} = $ ⬜⬜

3 marks

7. What is $3 \times 2\frac{3}{7}$? Write your answer as a mixed number in its simplest form.

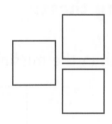

1 mark

8. Work out these divisions. Each answer will have a remainder.

a) $4531 \div 5$ b) $7406 \div 8$

2 marks

How did you do?

Score: ⬜

Quick Fire

Try to work out the answers to these in your head.

1. a) 45 ÷ 9 = ...

    b) 6 × 9 = ...

    c) 99 ÷ 9 = ...

    d) 9 × 9 = ...

    _____
    2 marks

2. a) 6446 – 330 = ...

    b) 5297 + 4700 = ...

    c) 2698 + 7200 = ...

    d) 8755 – 550 = ...

    _____
    2 marks

Now try these:

3. Fill in the missing numbers in the calculations below.

    a) 80% = $\dfrac{\boxed{}}{100}$

    b) 45% = $\dfrac{\boxed{}}{100}$

    _____
    2 marks

4. Round these numbers to the nearest whole number.

    a) 14.92 rounds to ....

    b) 35.49 rounds to ....

    c) 59.68 rounds to ....

    _____
    3 marks

62

5. What is $6 \times \frac{4}{9}$? Write your answer as a mixed number in its simplest form.

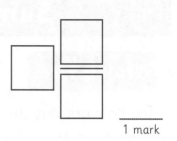

1 mark

6. Fill in the missing numbers in the calculations below.

a) $3\% = \dfrac{\boxed{}}{100}$

b) $68\% = \dfrac{\boxed{}}{100}$

2 marks

7. Circle the two numbers below which round to 54.7 to one decimal place.

53.84   54.64   54.66

     54.78   54.74

2 marks

8. Work out:

a) 836 528 + 9202

b) 547 998 + 22 610

2 marks

How did you do?

Score:

Quick Fire

Try to work out the answers to these in your head.

1. a) $0.7 \times 100 =$ ....
    b) $25.95 \times 10 =$ ....

    c) $11.1 \times 100 =$ ....
    d) $3.873 \times 1000 =$ ....

_____
2 marks

2. a) $-8 + 5 =$ ....
    b) $5 - 11 =$ ....

    c) $15 - 16 =$ ....
    d) $-12 + 9 =$ ....

_____
2 marks

3. Write the following decimals as fractions.

    a) $0.73 = \dfrac{}{}$
    b) $0.09 = \dfrac{}{}$

_____
2 marks

Now try these:

4. Write these percentages as decimals.

    a) $20\% =$ ....

    b) $65\% =$ ....

    c) $4\% =$ ....

_____
3 marks

5. Fill in the missing numbers below.

a) $\frac{1}{5}$ = 0.......... = ...%

b) $\dfrac{\boxed{}}{5}$ = 0.6 = ...%

2 marks

6. Count **backwards** in steps of 9 to fill in the blanks.

16   7   ....   −29

2 marks

7. Work out:

a) 3844 × 24   b) 4176 × 38

```
      3 8 4 4
  ×     2 4
  _____


  + _____
  _____
```

2 marks

8. Fill in the missing numbers in the calculation below.

$\frac{8}{13}$ + $\frac{11}{13}$ = $\boxed{}\dfrac{\boxed{}}{13}$

1 mark

How did you do?   Score: $\boxed{}$

65

10

Try to work out the answers to these in your head.

1. a) $9 \times 8 =$ ....

    b) $144 \times 0 =$ ....

    c) $81 \div 1 =$ ....

    d) $132 \div 11 =$ ....

    2 marks

2. Round these numbers to the nearest whole number.

    a) 14.92 rounds to ....

    b) 35.49 rounds to ....

    2 marks

Now try these:

3. Write these fractions as decimals.

    a) $\dfrac{8}{20} =$ ....

    b) $\dfrac{12}{25} =$ ....

    2 marks

4. Count **forwards** in steps of 12 to fill in the blanks.

    −22   26

    2 marks

5. Work out:

   a) $3^3 =$ ....

   b) $5^3 =$ ....

2 marks

6. Write these fractions as percentages.

   a) $\dfrac{25}{50} = \dfrac{\Box}{10} =$ .... %

   b) $\dfrac{72}{90} = \dfrac{\Box}{10} =$ .... %

2 marks

7. Put the numbers below in order from **smallest** to **largest**.

   65.897   65.879   65.898   65.799

   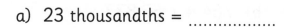

   ....

   smallest   largest

2 marks

8. Write the decimal equivalents of these numbers.

   a) 23 thousandths = ...

   b) 406 thousandths = ...

2 marks

How did you do?   Score: [   ]

Summer Term: Workout 9

Quick Fire

Try to work out the answers to these in your head.

1. a) 0.6 × 10 = ...   b) 72 ÷ 10 = ...

    c) 365 ÷ 10 = ...   d) 0.499 × 10 = ...

2 marks

2. a) 1537 × 1 = ...   b) 0.94 × 42 × 0 = ...

    c) 429 ÷ 1 = ...   d) 12 × 12 × 1 = ...

2 marks

3. Round these numbers to the nearest whole number.

    a) 23.51 → ....   b) 73.48 → ....

2 marks

Now try these:

4. Work out:

    a) 9056.46 – 2908.5   b) 764.4 + 67.833

2 marks

5. Fill in the missing numbers below.

a) $\frac{2}{5}$ = 0.......... = ...%

b) $\frac{\boxed{}}{5}$ = 0.......... = 80%

2 marks

6. Put the numbers below in order from **smallest** to **largest**.

833 754   833 764   833 745   833 755

....
smallest   largest

2 marks

7. Work out:

a) 38 082 + 45 065   b) 59 516 – 53 664

2 marks

8. Work out:

a) 885 ÷ 3   b) 934 ÷ 7

2 marks

How did you do?   Score:

Summer Term: Workout 11

Quick Fire

Try to work out the answers to these in your head.

1. a) $50 \times 900 =$ ....

   b) $63\,000 \div 7 =$ ....

   c) $77\,000 \div 110 =$ ....

   d) $6000 \times 120 =$ ....

   2 marks

2. a) $-7 + 16 =$ ....

   b) $8 - 11 =$ ....

   c) $13 - 19 =$ ....

   d) $-3 + 25 =$ ....

   2 marks

Now try these:

3. a) $112\,530 + 57\,000 =$ ....

   b) $632\,505 + 240\,000 =$ ....

   2 marks

4. What is $5 \times \frac{7}{13}$? Write your answer as a mixed number.

$$5 \times \frac{7}{13} = \boxed{} \; \frac{\boxed{}}{\boxed{}}$$

1 mark

5. Work out:

    a) 157 973 + 805 872   b) 622 267 − 145 545

6. Fill in the boxes with **>** or **<** to make each sentence true.

    a) 54 545 ☐ 54 454   b) 760 294 ☐ 760 429

7. Work out:

    a) 320.067 + 84.56   b) 912.37 + 8.783

8. Round these numbers to the nearest hundred thousand.

    a) 88 154 rounds to ....

    b) 574 986 rounds to ....

    c) 326 874 rounds to ....

How did you do?   **Score:** ☐

Quick Fire

Try to work out the answers to these in your head.

1. a) 9780 – 650 = ...   b) 8445 – 7400 = ...

    c) 2788 + 6100 = ...   d) 6541 + 460 = ...

    _____
    2 marks

2. Write the following decimals as fractions.

    a) 0.39 = ⬜/⬜   b) 0.04 = ⬜/⬜

    _____
    2 marks

Now try these:

3. What is 873.085 – 38.79?

_____
1 mark

4. Work out:

    a) 4752 ÷ 8   b) 6924 ÷ 6

    _____
    2 marks

5. Work out:

   a) $6^2 + 13 =$ ....

   b) $4^3 - 2 =$ ....

2 marks

6. Round these numbers to the nearest ten thousand.

   a) 548 366 → ....

   b) 481 989 → ....

   c) 114 930 → ....

3 marks

7. Put the numbers below in order from **largest** to **smallest**.

   39.131   39.313   39.311   39.113

   ....

   largest   smallest

2 marks

8. Work out:

   a) 6425 × 15

   b) 8115 × 26

2 marks

How did you do?   Score:

You've finished the workouts! Practise your skills by solving these puzzles.

Ben is keeping an eye on two lighthouses as he sails past.
One of the lighthouses flashes every 3 seconds.
The other lighthouse flashes every 5 seconds.
Ben starts his stopwatch after he sees them flash together.

How many more times do they flash together in the next 50 seconds?

.... times

Ben's boat has a number on its sail which:

- has no prime digits.

- is less than $\frac{8}{25}$ of 1000

- has digits that add up to a multiple of 6

Circle Ben's boat.

486

194

282

204

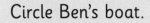

804

189

156

148

Puzzle Complete?

Answers

Autumn Term

Workout 1 — pages 2-3

1. a) **12** b) **36**
   c) **54** d) **66**
   2 marks for all four correct,
   otherwise 1 mark for at least two correct

2. a) **27** ÷ 9 = 3 b) **45** ÷ 9 = 5
   c) **81** ÷ 9 = 9 d) **108** ÷ 9 = 12
   1 mark for each correct answer

3. 75 100 **125 150 175** 200
   2 marks for all three correct,
   otherwise 1 mark for two correct

4. a) **0.25** b) **0.5** c) **0.75**
   2 marks for all three correct,
   otherwise 1 mark for two correct

5. a) $\frac{7}{8}$ 1 mark b) $\frac{7}{12}$ 1 mark

6. **911 945 1307 1310**
   2 marks for all four correct, otherwise
   1 mark for three in the correct order

7. a) $\begin{array}{r} 6\,4\,7\,2 \\ +\,2\,3\,5\,2 \\ \hline \mathbf{8\,8\,2\,4} \\ \scriptstyle 1 \end{array}$ b) $\begin{array}{r} 4\,2\,3\,1 \\ +\ \ 8\,2\,5 \\ \hline \mathbf{5\,0\,5\,6} \\ \scriptstyle 1 \end{array}$
   1 mark for each correct answer

Workout 2 — pages 4-5

1. a) **84** b) **0**
   c) **59** d) **1**
   2 marks for all four correct,
   otherwise 1 mark for at least two correct

2. a) **2** × 7 = 14 b) **3** × 7 = 21
   c) **8** × 7 = 56 d) **12** × 7 = 84
   1 mark for each correct answer

3. 12 6 **0 −6** −12 **−18**
   2 marks for all three correct,
   otherwise 1 mark for two correct

4. a) 8 × 13 = **13** × 8 1 mark
   b) **15** × 4 = 4 × 15 1 mark

5. $\frac{\mathbf{44}}{\mathbf{100}}$ $\frac{45}{100}$ $\frac{\mathbf{46}}{\mathbf{100}}$ $\frac{\mathbf{47}}{\mathbf{100}}$ $\frac{48}{100}$
   2 marks for all three correct,
   otherwise 1 mark for two correct

6. a) **1.8** 1 mark b) **0.7** 1 mark

7. a) $\begin{array}{r} 6\,1 \\ \times\ \ 8 \\ \hline \mathbf{4\,8\,8} \end{array}$ 1 mark b) $\begin{array}{r} 2\,8 \\ \times\ \ 7 \\ \hline \mathbf{1\,9\,6} \\ \scriptstyle 5 \end{array}$ 1 mark

Workout 3 — pages 6-7

1. a) **24** 1 mark b) **36** 1 mark
   c) **45** 1 mark d) **0** 1 mark

2. a) **24** ÷ 12 = 2 b) **48** ÷ 12 = 4
   c) **108** ÷ 12 = 9 d) **144** ÷ 12 = 12
   2 marks for all four correct,
   otherwise 1 mark for at least two correct

3. 99 108 **117** 126 **135** 144
   1 mark for both correct

4. a) 4572 < 4589 1 mark
   b) 7364 < 7368 1 mark

5. $\begin{array}{r} {}^{8}\!\not{9}\,{}^{1}2\,{}^{3}\!\not{4}\,{}^{1}6 \\ -\,5\,4\,3\,7 \\ \hline \mathbf{3\,8\,0\,9} \end{array}$ 1 mark

6. a) 1.26 < 2.01 1 mark
   b) 1.18 > 1.14 1 mark

7. a) **7.2** 1 mark b) **2.2** 1 mark

8. a) $\begin{array}{r} 2\,8\,2 \\ \times\ \ \ 3 \\ \hline \mathbf{8\,4\,6} \\ \scriptstyle 2 \end{array}$ 1 mark b) $\begin{array}{r} 1\,9\,1 \\ \times\ \ \ 7 \\ \hline \mathbf{1\,3\,3\,7} \\ \scriptstyle 6 \end{array}$ 1 mark

Workout 4 — pages 8-9

1. a) **24** b) **77**
   c) **60** d) **48**
   2 marks for all four correct,
   otherwise 1 mark for at least two correct

2. a) **1.5** 1 mark b) **6.4** 1 mark
   c) **3** 1 mark d) **0.8** 1 mark

3. 27 105 26 105 **25 105 24 105 23 105**
   2 marks for all three correct,
   otherwise 1 mark for two correct

4. a) 15 × 3 = **10** × 3 + **5** × 3 = 30 + 15 = **45**
   b) 21 × 4 = **20** × 4 + **1** × 4 = 80 + 4 = **84**
   1 mark for each correct answer

5. **7.3 7.7 7.8 8.0 8.2**
   2 marks for all five correct, otherwise
   1 mark for four in the correct order

© CGP — not to be photocopied

75

Answers

6. a) **0.1**   b) **0.4**
   c) **0.7**   d) **0.9**
   2 marks for all four correct, otherwise
   1 mark for at least two correct

7. a)
$$\begin{array}{r} 4\,{}^5\!\!\not6\,{}^1\!5\,8 \\ -\,2\,1\,6\,4 \\ \hline \mathbf{2\,4\,9\,4} \end{array}$$
   b)
$$\begin{array}{r} {}^8\!\!\not9\,{}^{10}\!\!\not7\,{}^1\!3\,6 \\ -\,4\,5\,9\,5 \\ \hline \mathbf{4\,5\,4\,1} \end{array}$$
   1 mark for each correct answer

Workout 5 — pages 10-11

1. a) **9**   b) **8**
   c) **7**   d) **12**
   2 marks for all four correct,
   otherwise 1 mark for at least two correct

2. a) **30** 1 mark   b) **88** 1 mark
   c) **0** 1 mark   d) **63** 1 mark

3. a)
$$\begin{array}{r} 5\,0\,2\,2\,7 \\ +\,1\,4\,2\,6\,1 \\ \hline \mathbf{6\,4\,4\,8\,8} \end{array}$$
   b)
$$\begin{array}{r} 6\,4\,2\,8\,0 \\ +\,2\,7\,2\,3\,1 \\ \hline \mathbf{9\,1\,5\,1\,1} \end{array}$$
   1 mark for each correct answer

4. 14   7   0   **−7**   **−14**   −21
   1 mark for both correct

5. a) **12 000**   b) **569 000**   c) **750 000**
   1 mark for each correct answer

6. a) 18.61 > 18.37   1 mark
   b) 10.66 > 10.57   1 mark

7. a)
$$\begin{array}{r} 1\,2\,8 \\ \times\quad 5 \\ \hline \mathbf{6\,4\,0} \end{array}$$
1 mark
   b)
$$\begin{array}{r} 8\,7\,1 \\ \times\quad 7 \\ \hline \mathbf{6\,0\,9\,7} \end{array}$$
1 mark

Workout 6 — pages 12-13

1. a) **24**   b) **49**
   c) **54**   d) **36**
   2 marks for all four correct,
   otherwise 1 mark for at least two correct

2. a) **145**   b) **0**
   c) **488**   d) **1**
   2 marks for all four correct,
   otherwise 1 mark for at least two correct

3. a) **9000**   b) **6700**   c) **7950**
   1 mark for each correct answer

4. a) **48 500**   b) **397 100**
   1 mark for each correct answer

5. a) $3\frac{6}{7}$ 1 mark   b) $4\frac{2}{5}$ 1 mark

6. 152 844   151 844
   150 844   **149 844**   **148 844**
   2 marks for all three correct,
   otherwise 1 mark for two correct

7. a) **2400**   b) **4800**   c) **570**
   1 mark for each correct answer

Workout 7 — pages 14-15

1. a) **36**   b) **40**
   c) **55**   d) **108**
   2 marks for all four correct,
   otherwise 1 mark for at least two correct

2. a) **0.6** 1 mark   b) **9.3** 1 mark
   c) **0.71** 1 mark   d) **0.02** 1 mark

3. a)
$$\begin{array}{r} 6\,3\,{}^7\!\!\not8\,{}^1\!3\,7 \\ -\,1\,3\,0\,4\,4 \\ \hline \mathbf{5\,0\,7\,9\,3} \end{array}$$
   b)
$$\begin{array}{r} 5\,3\,{}^8\!\!\not9\,{}^{17}\!\!\not8\,2 \\ -\,3\,3\,7\,9\,6 \\ \hline \mathbf{2\,0\,1\,8\,6} \end{array}$$
   1 mark for each correct answer

4. a) **72 000**   b) **847 000**
   1 mark for each correct answer

5. **341 551**   340 551
   339 551   **338 551**   337 551
   2 marks for all three correct,
   otherwise 1 mark for two correct

6. a) **1** 1 mark   b) **24** 1 mark

7. a)
$$\begin{array}{r} 9\,0\,3 \\ \times\quad 3 \\ \hline \mathbf{2\,7\,0\,9} \end{array}$$
   b)
$$\begin{array}{r} 4\,5\,1 \\ \times\quad 9 \\ \hline \mathbf{4\,0\,5\,9} \end{array}$$
   1 mark for each correct answer

Workout 8 — pages 16-17

1. a) **4**   b) **7**
   c) **9**   d) **12**
   2 marks for all four correct,
   otherwise 1 mark for at least two correct

2. a) **48** 1 mark   b) **22** 1 mark
   c) **54** 1 mark   d) **0** 1 mark

3. 129 024   229 024
   329 024   **429 024**   **529 024**
   2 marks for all three correct,
   otherwise 1 mark for two correct

4. **41 386**   **32 507**   **32 497**   **31 597**   **31 589**
   2 marks for all five correct, otherwise
   1 mark for four in the correct order

5. a) $1\frac{4}{9}$ 1 mark   b) $1\frac{1}{6}$ 1 mark

6. a) **0.01**   b) **0.07**   c) **0.45**
   2 marks for all three correct,
   otherwise 1 mark for two correct

7. a)   4 2 1 4 8   b)   9 4 2 5 4
      + 2 6 5 0 8   + 3 7 3 1 6
      ‾‾‾‾‾‾‾‾‾‾   ‾‾‾‾‾‾‾‾‾‾
        6 8 6 5 6   1 3 1 5 7 0
            1   1   1
   1 mark for each correct answer

Workout 9 — pages 18-19

1. a) **4300**   b) **7800**
   c) **9440**   d) **6987** .
   2 marks for all four correct,
   otherwise 1 mark for at least two correct

2. a) **2400**   b) **2620**
   c) **2104**   d) **382**
   2 marks for all four correct,
   otherwise 1 mark for at least two correct

3. a)   5 9 0 3 3 0   b)   3 8 2 1 6 0
      + 2 4 3 4 2 4   + 3 1 9 1 5 6
      ‾‾‾‾‾‾‾‾‾‾‾‾   ‾‾‾‾‾‾‾‾‾‾‾‾
        8 3 3 7 5 4   7 0 1 3 1 6
            1   1 1   1
   1 mark for each correct answer

4. a) **545 630**   1 mark
   b) **546 000**   1 mark

5. a) 32.7 < 34.7   1 mark
   b) 81.34 < 81.36   1 mark

6. a) **8.1**   1 mark   b) **4.6**   1 mark

7. **88 302   88 401   89 201   94 212   94 221**
   2 marks for all five correct, otherwise
   1 mark for four in the correct order

8. a)   2 9 2   b)   5 1 4
       ×   3   ×   6
      ‾‾‾‾‾‾‾‾   ‾‾‾‾‾‾‾‾
        8 7 6   1 mark   3 0 8 4   1 mark
          2   2

Workout 10 — pages 20-21

1. a) **50**   b) **80**
   c) **105**   d) **121**
   2 marks for all four correct,
   otherwise 1 mark for at least two correct

2. a) 15 ÷ **10** = 1.5   b) 6 ÷ **100** = 0.06
   c) 9 ÷ **10** = 0.9   d) 78 ÷ **100** = 0.78
   1 mark for each correct answer

3. **814 463   814 643   814 655   816 643**
   2 marks for all four correct, otherwise
   1 mark for three in the correct order

4. a) **25 000**   1 mark
   b) **59 510**   1 mark

5. 844 912   **744 912**
   644 912   **544 912   444 912**
   2 marks for all three correct,
   otherwise 1 mark for two correct

6. a) **40 700**   1 mark
   b) **12 320**   1 mark

7. a)   3 6 5⁶7¹2   b)   ⁶7⁵6̶6¹2¹1
      − 2 4 5 3 4   − 3 8 7 1 6
      ‾‾‾‾‾‾‾‾‾‾   ‾‾‾‾‾‾‾‾‾‾
        1 2 0 3 8   3 7 9 0 5
   1 mark for each correct answer

Workout 11 — pages 22-23

1. a) **35**   b) **36**
   c) **44**   d) **96**
   2 marks for all four correct,
   otherwise 1 mark for at least two correct

2. a) 3260 − **2000** = 1260   1 mark
   b) 4888 − **1000** = 3888   1 mark
   c) 8117 − **6000** = 2117   1 mark
   d) 9839 − **9000** = 839   1 mark

3. a)   3 7⁷8̶7̶2 3   b)   4⁴4̶4̶3³¹1 7 8
      − 1 6 4 8 1 2   − 3 1 9 3 3 0
      ‾‾‾‾‾‾‾‾‾‾‾‾   ‾‾‾‾‾‾‾‾‾‾‾‾
        2 1 3 9 1 1   1 2 5 8 4 8
   1 mark for each correct answer

4. **517 884**   617 884
   717 884   **817 884   917 884**
   2 marks for all three correct,
   otherwise 1 mark for two correct

5. a) **32 250**   b) **87 568**
   1 mark for both correct

6. a) **2**   b) **13**   c) **37**
   1 mark for each correct answer

7. a)   7 1 2   b)   8 6 5
       ×   5   ×   9
      ‾‾‾‾‾‾‾‾   ‾‾‾‾‾‾‾‾
        3 5 6 0   1 mark   7 7 8 5   1 mark
            1   5 4

Workout 12 — pages 24-25

1. a) 72 ÷ **100** = 0.72   1 mark
   b) 5 ÷ **10** = 0.5   1 mark
   c) 22 ÷ **10** = 2.2   1 mark
   d) 9 ÷ **100** = 0.09   1 mark

Answers

2. a) **27**   b) **60**
   c) **63**   d) **132**
   2 marks for all four correct,
   otherwise 1 mark for at least two correct

3. 273 612   283 612
   293 612   **303 612**   **313 612**
   2 marks for all three correct,
   otherwise 1 mark for two correct

4. a) $\frac{3}{10}$ 1 mark   b) $\frac{9}{10}$ 1 mark

5. a) **849 600**   1 mark
   b) **850 000**   1 mark

6. a) 154 381 − **60 000** = 94 381   1 mark
   b) **98 822** − 70 000 = 28 822   1 mark

7. a)   7 9 6 6 3 2   b)   8 0 9 0 5 3
    + 1 3 8 5 6 5   + 2 6 9 8 4 7
       9 3 5 1 9 7   **1 0 7 8 9 0 0**
         1 1 1   1 1 1
   1 mark for each correct answer

Spring Term

Workout 1 — pages 26-27

1. a) **30**   b) **21**   c) **56**
   d) **4**   e) **36**   f) **88**
   3 marks for all six correct, otherwise
   2 marks for at least four correct, or
   1 mark for at least two correct

2. a) **4800**   b) **160**
   c) **900**   d) **3600**
   2 marks for all four correct,
   otherwise 1 mark for at least two correct

3. a) **1050** 1 mark   b) **45** 1 mark
   c) **78.4** 1 mark   d) **2.04** 1 mark

4. a) **11.806** 1 mark   b) **2.186** 1 mark

5. 324 265   **324 858**   **342 885**   **343 588**
   2 marks for all four correct, otherwise
   1 mark for three in the correct order

6. $\frac{80}{100}$ $\frac{79}{100}$ $\frac{78}{100}$ $\frac{77}{100}$ $\frac{76}{100}$
   1 mark for all correct

7. a) $^{8}\!\not{9}^{1}1\,6\,6\,8\,3$ b) $5^{6}\not{7}^{1}2^{1}5\,5\,9$
    − 1 5 0 3 4 2   − 5 2 8 7 4 6
       7 6 6 3 4 1   **4 3 8 1 3**
   1 mark for each correct answer

Workout 2 — pages 28-29

1. a) **3 260 000**   b) **6 480 000**
   1 mark for both correct

2. a) **2**   b) **8**   c) **8**   d) **9**
   2 marks for all four correct,
   otherwise 1 mark for at least two correct

3. a)   4 3 8 0 0 7   b)   7 0 2 0 2 0
    +   3 3 7 2   +   3 5 9 9 6
      4 4 1 3 7 9   **7 3 8 0 1 6**
        1   1 1
   1 mark for each correct answer

4. a) **860 000**   b) **160 000**   c) **310 000**
   1 mark for each correct answer

5. **615 884**   616 884   617 884   **618 884**
   1 mark for both correct

6. a) $\frac{1}{2}$ b) $\frac{3}{4}$
   1 mark for each correct answer

7. a) 0.25 < 0.52   b) 1.7 > 1.07
   1 mark for each correct answer

8. a) 1619 − **700** = 919   1 mark
   b) **5465** − 3000 = 2465   1 mark
   c) 46 217 − **5000** = 41 217   1 mark

Workout 3 — pages 30-31

1. a) **11 000**   b) **30 100**
   c) **780 000**   d) **912 000**
   2 marks for all four correct,
   otherwise 1 mark for at least two correct

2. a) **0**   b) **841**   c) **1**   d) **469**
   2 marks for all four correct,
   otherwise 1 mark for at least two correct

3. a) **465** 1 mark   b) **56** 1 mark

4. a) $\frac{67}{100}$ 1 mark   b) $\frac{3}{100}$ 1 mark

5. a)   2 1 . 4 5 0   b) $^{0}\not{1}^{1}4.9^{4}\not{8}^{1}1$
    +   6 . 6 4 5   −   8 . 7 1 3
      2 8 . 0 9 5   **6 . 2 3 8**
          1
   1 mark for each correct answer

6. **178 509**, **188 509**, 198 509, **208 509**, 218 509
   2 marks for all three correct,
   otherwise 1 mark for two correct

7. **1.3**   **0.3**   **0.29**   **0.03**
   2 marks for all four correct, otherwise
   1 mark for three in the correct order

8. a)
```
    4 0 1
  ×     4
  ───────
  1 6 0 4
```
b)
```
    1 2 1
  ×     6
  ───────
    7 2 6
      1
```
1 mark for each correct answer

Workout 4 — pages 32-33

1. a) **77**   b) **56**
    c) **12**   d) **45**
    2 marks for all four correct,
    otherwise 1 mark for at least two correct

2. a) $1\frac{2}{7}$ 1 mark   b) $3\frac{3}{11}$ 1 mark

3. a) **200 000**   b) **700 000**
    c) **200 000**   d) **800 000**
    1 mark for each correct answer

4. a)
```
  7 2 9 ⁸9̶ ¹0
  − 4 0 1 4 3
  ───────────
    3 2 8 4 7
```
b)
```
  7 1 ⁴5̶ ¹³3̶ ¹⁸9̶ ¹3
  −       2 9 9 6
  ───────────────
    7 1 2 4 9 7
```
1 mark for each correct answer

5. a)
```
    4 5 3 . 4 3 0
  +     2 8 . 6 7 3
  ─────────────────
    4 8 2 . 1 0 3
          1 1 1
```
b)
```
    6 3 8 . 7 5 4
  + 1 7 8 . 2 1 0
  ─────────────────
    8 1 6 . 9 6 4
          1 1 1
```
1 mark for each correct answer

6. a)
```
    8 5 0
  ×     3
  ───────
  2 5 5 0
      1
```
b)
```
    1 3 2
  ×     7
  ───────
    9 2 4
      2 1
```
1 mark for each correct answer

7. **−24** −15 **−6** **3** 12
    2 marks for all three correct,
    otherwise 1 mark for two correct

Workout 5 — pages 34-35

1. a) **24**   b) **81**
    c) **24**   d) **77**
    2 marks for all four correct,
    otherwise 1 mark for at least two correct

2. a) **120**   b) **900**
    1 mark for both correct

3. a) **3670** 1 mark   b) **680** 1 mark
    c) **4.58** 1 mark   d) **0.36** 1 mark

4. a)
```
    8 4 6 7
  ×       2
  ─────────
  1 6 9 3 4
      1 1
```
b)
```
    9 3 1 5
  ×       4
  ─────────
  3 7 2 6 0
      1 2
```
1 mark for each correct answer

---

5. **297 106   276 109   267 190   267 109**
    2 marks for all four correct, otherwise
    1 mark for three in the correct order

6. a) $\frac{43}{100}$ 1 mark   b) $\frac{67}{100}$ 1 mark

7.
```
  9 ⁷8̶ ¹5 5 . ⁶7̶ ¹⁸9̶ ¹1
  −   6 0 6 . 4 9 3
  ───────────────────
      3 7 9 . 2 9 8   1 mark
```

8. a)
```
    3 1 1 9 8 2
  +   3 0 5 6 6
  ─────────────
    3 4 2 5 4 8
          1 1
```
b)
```
    2 4 1 2 3 2
  +     4 8 7 0
  ─────────────
    2 4 6 1 0 2
          1 1
```
1 mark for each correct answer

Workout 6 — pages 36-37

1. a) **67 000** 1 mark   b) **94 000** 1 mark

2. a) **5.4** 1 mark   b) **0.9** 1 mark
    c) **0.21** 1 mark   d) **0.6** 1 mark

3. a)
```
        3 1 2
    3│9 3 6
```
b)
```
        1 3 1
    6│7 ¹8 6
```
1 mark for each correct answer

4. 428 556 418 556 **408 556** **398 556**
    1 mark for both correct

5. a)
```
    ²3̶ ¹5 9 3 ²1̶ ¹6
  −     7 6 3 0 9
  ───────────────
    2 8 3 0 1 7
```
b)
```
  9 ²3̶ ¹³4̶ ¹⁰1̶ ¹3
  −     9 6 9 0
  ─────────────
  9 2 4 4 5 3
```
1 mark for each correct answer

6. a) **660 000**   b) **940 000**   c) **550 000**
    1 mark for each correct answer

7. **79 398**   **79 484**   **79 488**   **79 498**
    2 marks for all four correct, otherwise
    1 mark for three in the correct order

Workout 7 — pages 38-39

1. a) **142 000**   b) **33 300**
    1 mark for each correct answer

2. −12   −8   **−4**   **0**   **4**
    2 marks for all three correct,
    otherwise 1 mark for two correct

3. $\frac{8}{15}$ $\frac{7}{10}$ $\frac{4}{5}$
    2 marks for all three correct,
    otherwise 1 mark for one correct

4. a) **180** 1 mark   b) **2400** 1 mark
    c) **5600** 1 mark   d) **28 000** 1 mark

Answers

5. a) **400 000**　　b) **700 000**
   1 mark for each correct answer

6. $\frac{5}{8}$　*1 mark*

7. a) **480** × 10 = 4800　*1 mark*
   b) **1.5** × 10 = 15　*1 mark*
   c) **3040** ÷ 10 = 304　*1 mark*
   d) **8.9** ÷ 10 = 0.89　*1 mark*

Workout 8 — pages 40-41

1. a) **12**　　b) **40**　　c) **84**
   d) **22**　　e) **21**　　f) **32**
   3 marks for all six correct, otherwise
   2 marks for at least four correct, or
   1 mark for at least two correct

2. a) **7235**　*1 mark*　　b) **5515**　*1 mark*
   c) **9760**　*1 mark*　　d) **7924**　*1 mark*

3. 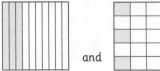　and
   1 mark for each correct answer

4. a)　　7 4 5 2 4　　b)　　5 4 7 6 3 7
   　　+　　9 8 7　　　　　+　　8 9 7 0
   　　7 5 5 1 1　　　　**5 5 6 6 0 7**
   　　　₁ ₁ ₁　　　　　　　₁ ₁ ₁
   1 mark for each correct answer

5. **703 848**, **603 848**, 503 848, **403 848**, 303 848
   2 marks for all three correct,
   otherwise 1 mark for two correct

6. a) **180.06**　　b) **55.97**　　c) **806.607**
   1 mark for each correct answer

7. a)　　　**5 9**　　　b)　　**1 2 5**
   　　4$\overline{)2^23^36}$　　　7$\overline{)8^17^35}$
   1 mark for each correct answer

Workout 9 — pages 42-43

1. a) **610 000**　　b) **993 000**　　c) **798 700**
   1 mark for each correct answer

2. a) **3**　　　　b) **6**
   c) **9**　　　　d) **4**
   2 marks for all four correct,
   otherwise 1 mark for at least two correct

3. $\frac{2}{5} = \frac{4}{10} = \frac{20}{50}$
   1 mark for each correct answer

4. a)　**1 8 0 r 2**　　b)　　**1 9 r 6**
   　3$\overline{)5^24\,2}$　　　9$\overline{)1^17^87}$
   1 mark for each correct answer

5. a) **2.6**　*1 mark*　　b) **1060**　*1 mark*

6. a) $\frac{7}{10}$　　b) $\frac{47}{100}$　　c) $\frac{9}{100}$
   1 mark for each correct answer

7. a)　　7 4 5 9　　b)　　4 6 7 4
   　　×　　　3　　　　×　　　8
   　　2 2 3 7 7　　　**3 7 3 9 2**
   　　　₁ ₁ ₂　　　　　₅ ₅ ₃
   1 mark for each correct answer

Workout 10 — pages 44-45

1. a) **2236**　　b) **3008**
   c) **6372**　　d) **9807**
   2 marks for all four correct,
   otherwise 1 mark for at least two correct

2. a) **157**　*1 mark*　　b) **3.81**　*1 mark*

3. a) **−5**　*1 mark*　　b) **−2**　*1 mark*
   c) **−7**　*1 mark*　　d) **−2**　*1 mark*

4. a)　　　**5 6 4**　　b)　　**1 4 9 2**
   　　2$\overline{)1^11^12\,8}$　　6$\overline{)8^29^55^12}$
   1 mark for each correct answer

5. $\frac{3}{4}$　　$\frac{11}{16}$　　$\frac{5}{8}$　　$\frac{1}{2}$
   2 marks for all four correct, otherwise
   1 mark for three in the correct order

6. a)　$^5\cancel{6}^12^7\cancel{7}16$　　b)　$3^2\cancel{3}^10^2\cancel{3}^1\cancel{3}^47$
   　　−　　3 3 4 5　　　−　　9 2 5 9
   　　5 9 3 7 1　　　**3 2 1 0 9 8**
   1 mark for each correct answer

7. a) $\frac{3}{8} = \frac{9}{24}$　　b) $\frac{4}{5} = \frac{20}{25}$
   1 mark for each correct answer

Workout 11 — pages 46-47

1. a) **40.9**　　b) **23**
   c) **816**　　d) **986**
   2 marks for all four correct,
   otherwise 1 mark for at least two correct

2. a) **495 623**　　b) **787 414**
   1 mark for each correct answer

3. a) $1\frac{1}{2} = \frac{3}{2}$ 1 mark

   b) $2\frac{3}{4} = \frac{11}{4}$ 1 mark

   c) $5\frac{2}{3} = \frac{17}{3}$ 1 mark

4. a)
```
    3 1 2
  ×   2 5
  1 5 6,0
  6 2 4 0
  7 8 0 0
      1
```
   b)
```
    1 6 3
  ×   4 6
  9,7,8
  6,5,2 0
  7 4 9 8
      1
```
   1 mark for each correct answer

5. E.g.

   1 mark for any 7 triangles shaded in
   the first shape and 1 mark for any 21
   hexagons shaded in the second shape

6. a) **400** 1 mark   b) **30** 1 mark
   c) **9** 1 mark   d) **60** 1 mark

7. a) **−12** 1 mark   b) **−17** 1 mark

Workout 12 — pages 48-49

1. a) **38**   b) **70**
   c) **64**   d) **39**
   2 marks for all four correct,
   otherwise 1 mark for at least two correct

2. a) **6** 1 mark   b) **5** 1 mark

3. a) $\frac{1}{2} + \frac{1}{8} = \frac{4}{8} + \frac{1}{8} = \frac{5}{8}$ 1 mark

   b) $\frac{11}{15} - \frac{3}{5} = \frac{11}{15} - \frac{9}{15} = \frac{2}{15}$ 1 mark

4. a) **7 8 2 r 2**
   $3\overline{)2^23^24\,8}$
   b) **1 0 2 3 r 4**
   $7\overline{)7\,1^16^25}$
   1 mark for each correct answer

5. a) **9.8** × 1000 = 9800 1 mark
   b) **81 000** ÷ 1000 = 81 1 mark
   c) **0.09** × 1000 = 90 1 mark

6. a)
```
    8 0 8 7 7 1
  + 5 1 7 4 9 8
  1 3 2 6 2 6 9
      1 1 1
```
   b)
```
    7 8 3 5 4 5
  + 1 3 1 9 8 4
    9 1 5 5 2 9
      1   1 1
```
   1 mark for each correct answer

7. $\frac{4}{7} = \frac{16}{28}$ 1 mark

8. a) $2\frac{5}{7} = \frac{19}{7}$ b) $4\frac{2}{5} = \frac{22}{5}$
   1 mark for each correct answer

Summer Term

Workout 1 — pages 50-51

1. a) **30**   b) **27**   c) **48**
   d) **42**   e) **64**   f) **132**
   3 marks for all six correct, otherwise
   2 marks for at least four correct, or
   1 mark for at least two correct

2. a) **5217**   b) **9434**
   c) **9001**   d) **8703**
   2 marks for all four correct,
   otherwise 1 mark for at least two correct

3. $\frac{9}{5}$ 1 mark

4. **549 711**, 449 711, **349 711**, **249 711**, 149 711
   2 marks for all three correct,
   otherwise 1 mark for two correct

5. a) **340 000**   b) **200 000**
   c) **850 000**   d) **750 000**
   1 mark for each correct answer

6. a)
```
    1 7 2.1 0 6
  +   6 5.8 9 5
    2 3 8.0 0 1
      1   1 1 1
```
   b)
```
    8 3 1.1 7 8
  −   4 2.5 4 0
    7 8 8.6 3 8
```
   1 mark for each correct answer

7. a)
```
    8 3 8 7 0
  −   4 3 2 1
    7 9 5 4 9
```
   b)
```
    9 6 1 7 1 5
  +   2 7 2 5 6
    9 8 8 9 7 1
              1
```
   1 mark for each correct answer

Workout 2 — pages 52-53

1. a) **4**   b) **12**   c) **7**
   d) **9**   e) **5**   f) **12**
   3 marks for all six correct, otherwise
   2 marks for at least four correct, or
   1 mark for at least two correct

2. a) **4**   b) **−5**
   c) **−3**   d) **8**
   2 marks for all four correct,
   otherwise 1 mark for at least two correct

3. a) **1** 1 mark   b) **3** 1 mark

4. $\frac{8}{9} + \frac{5}{9} = \frac{13}{9} = 1\frac{4}{9}$ 1 mark

Answers

5. a) 153
  × 18
  1 2₄2₂4
  1 5 3 0
  2 7 5 4

  b) 342
  × 24
  1 3,6 8
  6 8 4 0
  8 2 0 8
  ₁ ₁

1 mark for each correct answer

6. $\frac{1}{4}$ $\frac{5}{16}$ $\frac{3}{8}$ $\frac{1}{2}$
2 marks for all four correct, otherwise
1 mark for three in the correct order

7. **8549** 18 549 **28 549** **38 549** 48 549
2 marks for all three correct,
otherwise 1 mark for two correct

8. a) **1 3 9**
   3⟌4¹1²7

   b) **2 3 8**
   4⟌9¹5³2

1 mark for each correct answer

Workout 3 — pages 54-55

1. a) **63** b) **5**
   c) **5** d) **144**
   2 marks for all four correct,
   otherwise 1 mark for at least two correct

2. a) **620 115** b) **309 338**
   1 mark for each correct answer

3. a) **25** 1 mark b) **64** 1 mark

4. $6\frac{2}{3}$ 1 mark

5. 33 209 **32 209** **31 209** **30 209** 29 209
   2 marks for all three correct,
   otherwise 1 mark for two correct

6. a) **900 000** 1 mark
   b) **500 000** 1 mark
   c) **700 000** 1 mark

7. a) **6 9 1**
   4⟌2²7³6 4

   b) **3 6 9**
   9⟌3³3⁶2⁸1

   1 mark for each correct answer

8. 389 **10 389** **20 389** **30 389** 40 389
   2 marks for all three correct,
   otherwise 1 mark for two correct

Workout 4 — pages 56-57

1. a) **48** b) **8**
   c) **12** d) **88**
   2 marks for all four correct,
   otherwise 1 mark for at least two correct

2. a) **48** b) **0**
   c) **0** d) **63**
   2 marks for all four correct,
   otherwise 1 mark for at least two correct

3. a) **3.3** b) **7.1** c) **6.3**
   1 mark for each correct answer

4. a) **8** 1 mark b) **64** 1 mark

5. 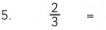 $\frac{2}{3}$ = $\frac{6}{9}$ = $\frac{12}{18}$

   1 mark for the correct fractions
   1 mark for the correct shading

6. **−7** **−2** **1** **3** **5**
   2 marks for all five correct, otherwise
   1 mark for four in the correct order

7. a) **9000** b) **90** c) **0.9**
   1 mark for each correct answer

Workout 5 — pages 58-59

1. a) **24** b) **80**
   c) **132** d) **0**
   2 marks for all four correct,
   otherwise 1 mark for at least two correct

2. a) **5300** b) **3180**
   c) **6308** d) **9911**
   2 marks for all four correct,
   otherwise 1 mark for at least two correct

3. a) **169 530** 1 mark
   b) **872 505** 1 mark

4. a) 1385
   × 33
   4,1,5,5
   4,1,5,50
   4 5 7 0 5
   ₁

   b) 2053
   × 24
   8 2,1,2
   4 1,060
   4 9 2 7 2

   1 mark for each correct answer

5. a) **10** b) **100** c) **100**
   1 mark for each correct answer

6. $\frac{6}{7} + \frac{6}{7} = \frac{12}{7} = 1\frac{5}{7}$ 1 mark

7. a) **0.012** 1 mark b) **0.27** 1 mark

8. a) $4\,7\,\overset{2}{\cancel{3}}\,\overset{1}{5}\,3$
   $-\,1\,2\,1\,6\,1$
   $\overline{3\,5\,1\,9\,2}$

   b) $\overset{6}{\cancel{7}}\,\overset{1}{2}\,5\,5\,8\,6$
   $-\,\,\,3\,4\,3\,5\,1$
   $\overline{6\,9\,1\,2\,3\,5}$

   1 mark for each correct answer

Workout 6 — pages 60-61

1. a) **2.4**   b) **0.36**
   c) **1.98**   d) **0.005**
   2 marks for all four correct,
   otherwise 1 mark for at least two correct

2. a) **−9**   b) **8**
   c) **0**   d) **−7**
   2 marks for all four correct,
   otherwise 1 mark for at least two correct

3. 46.779 > 46.778   1 mark
   3.14 < 3.141   1 mark

4. a) **9** 1 mark   b) **49** 1 mark

5. **21.493   21.43   21.429   21.349**
   2 marks for all four correct, otherwise
   1 mark for three in the correct order

6. a) $\dfrac{17}{11}$ b) $\dfrac{19}{7}$ c) $\dfrac{19}{4}$
   1 mark for each correct answer

7. $7\dfrac{2}{7}$ 1 mark

8. a) $\quad\ \ \mathbf{9\,0\,6\,r\,1}$
   $5\overline{)4\,\overset{4}{5}\,3\,\overset{3}{1}}$

   b) $\quad\ \ \mathbf{9\,2\,5\,r\,6}$
   $8\overline{)7\,\overset{7}{4}\,\overset{2}{0}\,\overset{}{6}}$

   1 mark for each correct answer

Workout 7 — pages 62-63

1. a) **5**   b) **54**
   c) **11**   d) **81**
   2 marks for all four correct,
   otherwise 1 mark for at least two correct

2. a) **6116**   b) **9997**
   c) **9898**   d) **8205**
   2 marks for all four correct,
   otherwise 1 mark for at least two correct

3. a) $\dfrac{80}{100}$ 1 mark   b) $\dfrac{45}{100}$ 1 mark

4. a) **15**   b) **35**   c) **60**
   1 mark for each correct answer

5. $2\dfrac{2}{3}$ 1 mark

6. a) $\dfrac{3}{100}$ 1 mark   b) $\dfrac{68}{100}$ 1 mark

7. **54.66** and **54.74** should be circled
   1 mark for each correct answer

8. a) $8\,3\,6\,5\,2\,8$
   $+\,\,\,\,\,\,9\,2\,0\,2$
   $\overline{8\,4\,5\,7\,3\,0}$
   $\,_1\,_1$

   b) $5\,4\,7\,9\,9\,8$
   $+\,\,\,2\,2\,6\,1\,0$
   $\overline{5\,7\,0\,6\,0\,8}$
   $\,_1\,_1\,_1$

   1 mark for each correct answer

Workout 8 — pages 64-65

1. a) **70**   b) **259.5**
   c) **1110**   d) **3873**
   2 marks for all four correct,
   otherwise 1 mark for at least two correct

2. a) **−3**   b) **−6**   c) **−1**   d) **−3**
   2 marks for all four correct,
   otherwise 1 mark for at least two correct

3. a) $\dfrac{73}{100}$ 1 mark   b) $\dfrac{9}{100}$ 1 mark

4. a) **0.2**   b) **0.65**   c) **0.04**
   1 mark for each correct answer

5. a) $\dfrac{1}{5} = 0.2 = \mathbf{20\%}$ 1 mark
   b) $\dfrac{3}{5} = 0.6 = \mathbf{60\%}$ 1 mark

6. 16   7   **−2**   **−11**   **−20**   −29
   2 marks for all three correct, otherwise
   1 mark for at least two correct

7. a) $\quad\ \ 3\,8\,4\,4$
   $\times\quad\ \ 2\,4$
   $\overline{1\,5\,\overset{3}{3}\,\overset{1}{7}\,\overset{}{6}}$
   $7\,\overset{}{6}\,8\,8\,0$
   $\overline{9\,2\,2\,5\,6}$
   $\,_1\,_1\,_1$

   b) $\quad\ \ 4\,1\,7\,6$
   $\times\quad\ \ 3\,8$
   $\overline{3\,3\,\overset{4}{4}\,\overset{0}{0}\,\overset{}{8}}$
   $1\,2\,5\,\overset{2}{2}\,8\,0$
   $\overline{1\,5\,8\,6\,8\,8}$

   1 mark for each correct answer

8. $1\dfrac{6}{13}$ 1 mark

Workout 9 — pages 66-67

1. a) **72**   b) **0**
   c) **81**   d) **12**
   2 marks for all four correct,
   otherwise 1 mark for at least two correct

2. a) **15** 1 mark   b) **35** 1 mark

3. a) **0.4** 1 mark   b) **0.48** 1 mark

4. −22   **−10**   **2**   **14**   26
   2 marks for all three correct,
   otherwise 1 mark for at least two correct

5. a) **27** 1 mark   b) **125** 1 mark

6. a) $\dfrac{5}{10} = \mathbf{50\%}$ b) $\dfrac{8}{10} = \mathbf{80\%}$
   1 mark for each correct answer

83

Answers

7. **65.799** **65.879** **65.897** **65.898**
2 marks for all four correct, otherwise
1 mark for three in the correct order

8. a) **0.023** 1 mark
b) **0.406** 1 mark

Workout 10 — pages 68-69

1. a) **6** b) **7.2**
c) **36.5** d) **4.99**
2 marks for all four correct,
otherwise 1 mark for at least two correct

2. a) **1537** b) **0**
c) **429** d) **144**
2 marks for all four correct,
otherwise 1 mark for at least two correct

3. a) **24** 1 mark b) **73** 1 mark

4. a) $\begin{array}{r} ^8{}^9{}^{10}9{}^4{}^{15}0\overset{1}{8}6.46 \\ -2\,9\,0\,8.5\,0 \\ \hline \mathbf{6\,1\,4\,7.9\,6} \end{array}$
b) $\begin{array}{r} 7\,6\,4.4\,0\,0 \\ +\ \ 6\,7.8\,3\,3 \\ \hline \mathbf{8\,3\,2.2\,3\,3} \\ \scriptstyle 1\ \ 1\ \ 1 \end{array}$
1 mark for each correct answer

5. a) $\frac{2}{5}$ = 0.**4** = **40%** 1 mark
b) $\frac{4}{5}$ = **0.8** = 80% 1 mark

6. **833 745** **833 754** **833 755** **833 764**
2 marks for all four correct, otherwise
1 mark for three in the correct order

7. a) $\begin{array}{r} 3\,8\,0\,8\,2 \\ +4\,5\,0\,6\,5 \\ \hline \mathbf{8\,3\,1\,4\,7} \\ \scriptstyle 1\ \ \ 1 \end{array}$
b) $\begin{array}{r} 5\,9\,5\,1\,6 \\ -5\,3\,6\,6\,4 \\ \hline \mathbf{5\,8\,5\,2} \end{array}$
1 mark for each correct answer

8. a) $\mathbf{2\,9\,5}$ over $3\overline{)8{}^2 8{}^1 5}$
b) $\mathbf{1\,3\,3}\,r\,3$ over $7\overline{)9{}^2 3{}^2 4}$
1 mark for each correct answer

Workout 11 — pages 70-71

1. a) **45 000** b) **9000**
c) **700** d) **720 000**
2 marks for all four correct,
otherwise 1 mark for at least two correct

2. a) **9** b) **–3**
c) **–6** d) **22**
2 marks for all four correct,
otherwise 1 mark for at least two correct

3. a) **169 530** 1 mark
b) **872 505** 1 mark

4. a) $2\frac{9}{13}$ 1 mark

5. a) $\begin{array}{r} 1\,5\,7\,9\,7\,3 \\ +8\,0\,5\,8\,7\,2 \\ \hline \mathbf{9\,6\,3\,8\,4\,5} \\ \scriptstyle 1\ 1\ 1 \end{array}$
b) $\begin{array}{r} {}^5\cancel{8}{}^1\cancel{2}{}^1\cancel{2}{}^1 2\,6\,7 \\ -1\,4\,5\,5\,4\,5 \\ \hline \mathbf{4\,7\,6\,7\,2\,2} \end{array}$
1 mark for each correct answer

6. a) 54 545 **>** 54 454 1 mark
b) 760 294 **<** 760 429 1 mark

7. a) $\begin{array}{r} 3\,2\,0.0\,6\,7 \\ +\ \ 8\,4.5\,6\,0 \\ \hline \mathbf{4\,0\,4.6\,2\,7} \\ \scriptstyle 1\ \ \ \ \ 1 \end{array}$
b) $\begin{array}{r} 9\,1\,2.3\,7\,0 \\ +\ \ \ \ 8.7\,8\,3 \\ \hline \mathbf{9\,2\,1.1\,5\,3} \\ \scriptstyle 1\ 1\ 1 \end{array}$
1 mark for each correct answer

8. a) **100 000** b) **600 000** c) **300 000**
1 mark for each correct answer

Workout 12 — pages 72-73

1. a) **9130** b) **1045**
c) **8888** d) **7001**
2 marks for all four correct,
otherwise 1 mark for at least two correct

2. a) $\frac{39}{100}$ 1 mark b) $\frac{1}{25}$ 1 mark

3. $\begin{array}{r} ^6 8 {}^{12}\cancel{7}{}^{10}3.{}^1\cancel{0}\,8\,5 \\ -\ \ 3\,8.7\,9\,0 \\ \hline \mathbf{8\,3\,4.2\,9\,5} \end{array}$
1 mark for each correct answer

4. a) $\mathbf{5\,9\,4}$ over $8\overline{)4{}^4 7{}^7 5{}^3 2}$
b) $\mathbf{1\,1\,5\,4}$ over $6\overline{)6\,9{}^3 2{}^2 4}$
1 mark for each correct answer

5. a) **49** 1 mark b) **62** 1 mark

6. a) **550 000** 1 mark
b) **480 000** 1 mark
c) **110 000** 1 mark

7. **39.313** **39.311** **39.131** **39.113**
2 marks for all four correct, otherwise
1 mark for three in the correct order

8. a) $\begin{array}{r} 6\,4\,2\,5 \\ \times\ \ \ \ 1\,5 \\ \hline 3\,2{}_1 1{}_2 2\,5 \\ 6\,4\,2\,5\,0 \\ \hline \mathbf{9\,6\,3\,7\,5} \\ \scriptstyle 1\ \ 1 \end{array}$
b) $\begin{array}{r} 8\,1\,1\,5 \\ \times\ \ \ \ 2\,6 \\ \hline 4\,8\,6\,9{}_3 0 \\ 1\,6\,2\,3{}_1 0\,0 \\ \hline \mathbf{2\,1\,0\,9\,9\,0} \\ \scriptstyle 1\ \ 1 \end{array}$
1 mark for each correct answer

Puzzles: Baffling Boats — page 74
The lighthouses flash together **3** times in the next 50s.
Ben's boat is number **189**

M5ARXW21